THIS IS A WAXCRAYON LTD BOOK

Text and design copyright © Waxcrayon Ltd 2015

First Edition
Published in 2015 by Waxcrayon Ltd
Unit 5, Dodnor Park, Newport, Isle of Wight, PO30 5XE

A catalogue record for this book is available from the British Library.

ISBN-13: 978-0-9575770-7-7

Author: Russell Ince
Artwork: Russell Ince
Editor: Matt Sarson

www.fairiesthebook.com

FAIRIES

THE BOOK OF SECRETS

WRITTEN & ILLUSTRATED BY

RUSSELL INCE

Contents

Introduction

As a child, I was a very keen footballer. I would spend endless hours kicking a ball around whenever I could find even the smallest patch of grass. Around the age of 10 or 11, I would often play at the park next to my house – "The Rec", as we used to call it. The Rec was encircled by untouched woodland and it was within its dense undergrowth that I first remember being touched by Fairy magic.

I had accidently kicked the ball into the trees and had to fight my way through the long, gangly branches, as I had a hundred times before. Here, I came upon a place where time suddenly stood still. A bubbling stream caressed the pebbled bed beneath it. Mossy rocks, verdant ferns and beautiful flowers were bathed in a sparkling sunshine that split into shards of light as it cut through the dense green canopy above. I stood for what seemed like hours immersed in the majesty of the place. After this experience, I spent years scouring every inch of the woodland trying to rediscover this enchanting vision once again. But, it wasn't until years later that I realised the significance of what had happened. On that day, I had been lucky enough to be one of the few human beings to be permitted entrance into the Fairy Realm.

It was another decade before I would have my second Fairy encounter. I was out riding my bike through the hills and had chosen a slightly different route to usual. It led me to a clearing in the forest, where an old stone cottage nestled amongst the trees. Here, once again, time seemed to stand still. The area was bathed in beams of warm golden light and hundreds of tiny creatures danced joyously through the air. A strange electric–like sensation tingled through every nerve in my body. I have since returned several times to this very spot and have never again experienced the magic I did that day.

I now jump to earlier this year, when my little girl had just turned three. Talk of Fairies was an everyday occurrence, as I am sure it is in most households with young children. I had "helped" the Fairies build a Fairy house on a grassy mound in the garden a year or two before. So, it came as no shock one spring morning when my little girl came running in saying – "Mummy, Daddy the Fairies have left a present in the Fairy house."

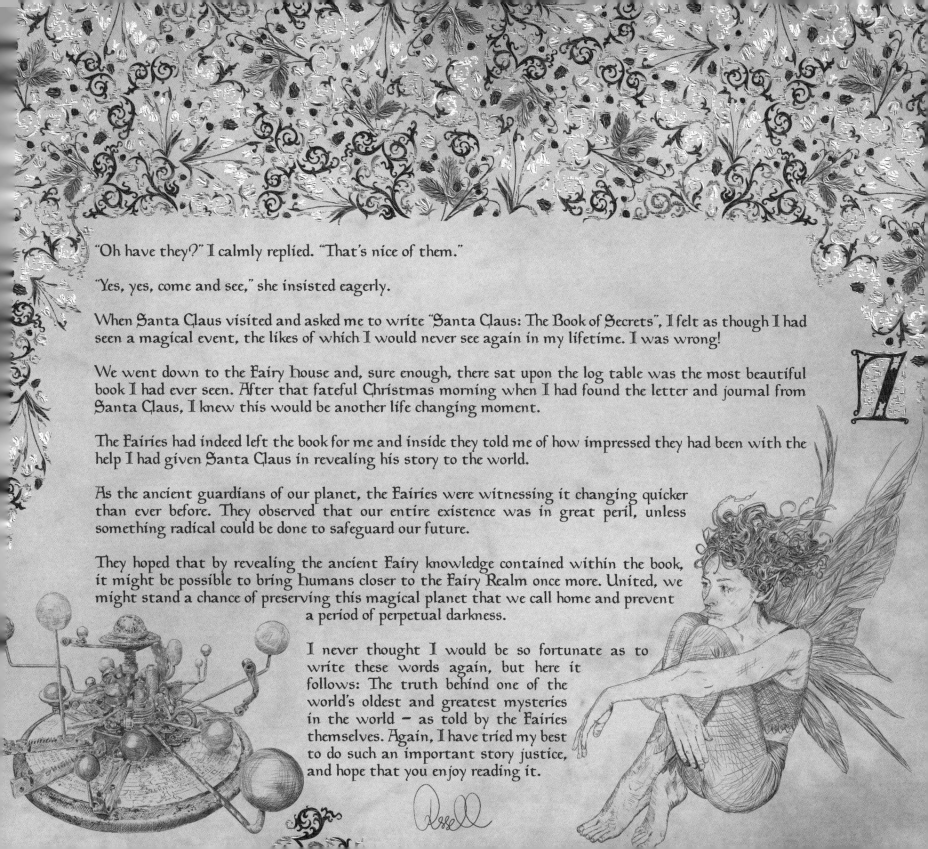

"Oh have they?" I calmly replied. "That's nice of them."

"Yes, yes, come and see," she insisted eagerly.

When Santa Claus visited and asked me to write "Santa Claus: The Book of Secrets", I felt as though I had seen a magical event, the likes of which I would never see again in my lifetime. I was wrong!

We went down to the Fairy house and, sure enough, there sat upon the log table was the most beautiful book I had ever seen. After that fateful Christmas morning when I had found the letter and journal from Santa Claus, I knew this would be another life changing moment.

The Fairies had indeed left the book for me and inside they told me of how impressed they had been with the help I had given Santa Claus in revealing his story to the world.

As the ancient guardians of our planet, the Fairies were witnessing it changing quicker than ever before. They observed that our entire existence was in great peril, unless something radical could be done to safeguard our future.

They hoped that by revealing the ancient Fairy knowledge contained within the book, it might be possible to bring humans closer to the Fairy Realm once more. United, we might stand a chance of preserving this magical planet that we call home and prevent a period of perpetual darkness.

I never thought I would be so fortunate as to write these words again, but here it follows: The truth behind one of the world's oldest and greatest mysteries in the world – as told by the Fairies themselves. Again, I have tried my best to do such an important story justice, and hope that you enjoy reading it.

History

What are Fairies? Where did they come from? How does their magic work? These are questions that have been subject to speculation amongst the human race since the beginning of time.

If you are hoping to read this and learn of beliefs, myths and Fairy rituals from around the world then I suggest that you put this book down now. There are many good books that have already been written which cover this. As Fairies ourselves, we have no intention of recounting these tales. If, however, you wish to learn the truth as told by Fairies, then may we invite you to read on. It is not our intention to disrespect the stories told by different cultures around the world, but to reveal information that has remained a mystery to mankind for centuries.

Firstly, we know that when humans utter the word "Fairies" you are normally referring to those of us who appear as tiny winged creatures. The Fairy Realm, however, is home to a rich diversity of magical beings. You may recognise some of these if we use the names you are more familiar with: Elves, Dwarves, Gnomes, Brownies, Nymphs, Sprites, Salamanders and Pixies are just some of the varieties of Fairy, or Fey Folk, as we all like to be known.

The Fey Folk make up some of the oldest species of creatures on the planet; our existence predates many life forms that now share our home. Whilst many of your most popular Fairy stories seem to originate from Europe, I can assure you that Fairies can be found the world over. Wherever nature can be found, so can we. Despite the common depiction of Fairies, in keeping with traditions originating from the areas you call Ireland, Cornwall, The Isle of Man, Scotland, Wales, Germany, Eastern Europe, Scandinavia and the Mediterranean, we always take on an appearance to fit in with the beliefs and traditions of a specific area. However your culture chooses to see Fairies, this is how they will appear to you. Therefore, in essence all beliefs are correct.

It would be many millions of years before humans arrived on Earth, and whilst we know where you came from, it is not our place to disclose this information. In your early years, you worshipped and respected nature, understanding your place in the Wheel of Life. You would actively seek our help, looking to learn from our wisdom and knowledge. You would leave offerings in return for blessings or a little good fortune.

The exchange of gifts between humans and Fairies was a frequent form of early trade. Nowadays, this relationship between us has all but gone; the majority of you have chosen to sever your connection with us, instead choosing to focus on your new technological world.

As you grew and developed, we foresaw the damage that your modern world would likely do to the planet. We tried once before, at the time of your industrial revolution, to forge a new relationship, so as to avert the damage that was being inflicted upon our beautiful world. After many years of our efforts going unheeded, many Fey Folk began to retreat from the human world. However, the time has come once more for us to rally and attempt to rebuild our bond. If we fail, the existence of us all will hang in a precarious balance.

It is you who holds the key to the future of our world. By reading this book, we hope that you will discover a little about who we are and what we do. Most importantly of all, we hope you begin to understand why it is so important that you let us back in to your lives. Together we may stand a chance of changing the fate of this wondrous planet, which is home to us all.

Fairy Realm

In the simplest terms, the Fairy Realm is a parallel world that exists independently of your own, while occupying the same space.

To try to help you to understand this, let me explain further. Our world exists on a different vibrational frequency, or wavelength, to your own — much the same as when you tune into different television stations. There are hundreds of programmes whizzing around your television set all of the time. You can only watch one at a time though and which one you see depends upon which you choose to tune into. It is the same with the human Realm and the Fairy Realm; we are just two of the many worlds that, whilst separate, are always around us.

You might not be aware that all over the world there is a network of hidden natural power lines that criss-cross the globe, linking a huge web of sacred, magical sites. These sites are where you will often find doorways, or portals, that enable travel between our realms. These magical doorways are not closed to humans as such, they just require a view of the world and a way of thinking that has long been lost to most of you.

Whilst we, of course, are aware of the locations of each of these magical portals, it is not yet safe for us to reveal them to you. We fear that if we were to do so, they may attract the wrong kind of attention. You might wish to discover the location of these doorways for yourselves and maybe catch a glimpse of us as we pass back and forth. The truth is, you may walk past one everyday or even play near one in your garden. In order for you to see the doorways, you must prove yourself to be worthy and pure of heart.

The only advice that we can offer is listen to your heart; it will rarely lead you astray. If a place feels magical, then it most likely is. The more you listen, the more you will hear.

FAiry LIVES

Fairies, as beings, live in two distinct ways. There are those that live and work in groups, known as "Trooping Fairies", and those that prefer to live and work in solitude. The latter only come together at magical times of the year, for festivals and celebrations. Each Troop has what you would call a King and Queen. They are usually the eldest, wisest and most respected Fairies, and have earned their position, rather than simply inherited it.

When in our physical form, we Fairies live in homes and houses just as you do. We do not have families as such, but enjoy a more communal existence. We have a strong sense of unity, both with nature and one another. Indeed, it is our connection to nature that means Fairy homes and villages are often found in magical natural surroundings, such as earth mounds, forests, waterfalls and caves, as well as upon ancient sites, such as stone circles.

The houses themselves are often made within an existing natural structure, such as the trunk of a tree. Our houses are always made only from what nature willingly provides. For example, we will never cut wood from a tree, but only use that which has been offered by the tree itself and fallen naturally.

The sites of many Fairy homes and villages have been held as sacred to humans for thousands of years. Have you ever thought about how your ancestors came to discover the exact location of these magical sites? Or considered who helped them to build the seemingly impossible monuments that stand upon some of them? Sites such as Stonehenge in England are a long-standing testament as to what can be achieved when Man and Fairy work in unison.

For millennia, us Fey Folk lived in close quarters with humans. But these were times when you lived your lives closer to nature. As your small settlements became villages, villages became towns and towns turned into sprawling cities, your numbers grew and your footprint on the world increased extensively. This rapid expansion forced many Fairies to retreat permanently into the Fairy Realm; afraid of the impact you were beginning to have.

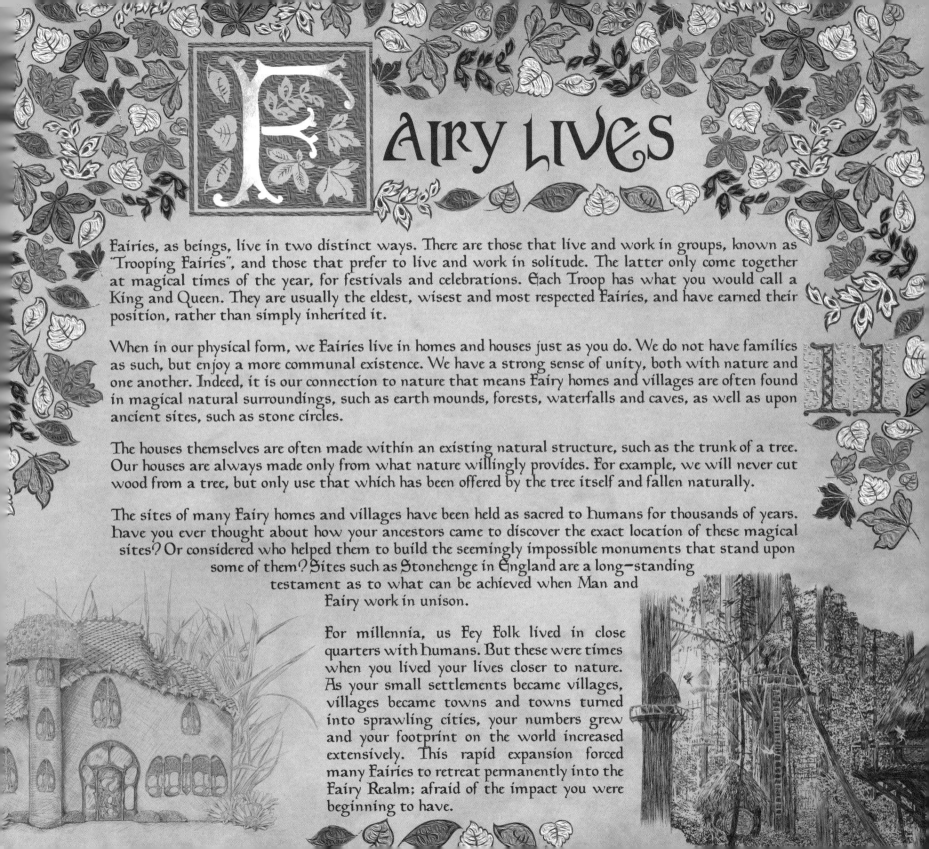

Appearance

Much is made of what Fairies really look like. The stereotypes ingrained in your tales and imagery, whilst all somewhat based upon the truth, barely scratch the surface of the diverse ways in which we can appear.

In our natural form, we are beings of pure energy and light, able to pass freely through the many realms of our world. however, we are also able to take on a physical form should we wish, in order to carry out many of our duties. Most Fey Folk are shape-shifters — able to change our appearance in whichever way we wish to suit the environment we are in.

This extends to the times when we may choose to appear to humans as well. Our form is completely fluid and changeable. It is your minds that dress our energy forms into something that you can easily comprehend, and hence we are often believed to have human characteristics. Also, because we are beings whose duty it is to protect all of nature, our clothing is always made, as are our houses, from natural materials. For example, discarded lamb or rabbit's wool caught on a bush can be made into felt and dyed with natural plant extracts to give a radiant colour. Along with the more common Fairy forms, we may also choose to take on the appearance of an animal. Whilst in your realm, this means that we are more able to blend in and escape any unwanted attention.

Fey Folk come in all shapes and sizes, but a term that has been applied to us throughout history has been 'The Little People'. As we mentioned, when choosing to appear to humans, we have always adopted a form that your mind feels comfortable with. This is why we think that you often see us as little people. Perhaps by making us appear smaller than yourselves, the unknown factor associated with the Fairy Realm may appear less threatening. We do not mind this at all, but you should always remember that just because something appears to look a certain way, it doesn't necessarily mean that it is so.

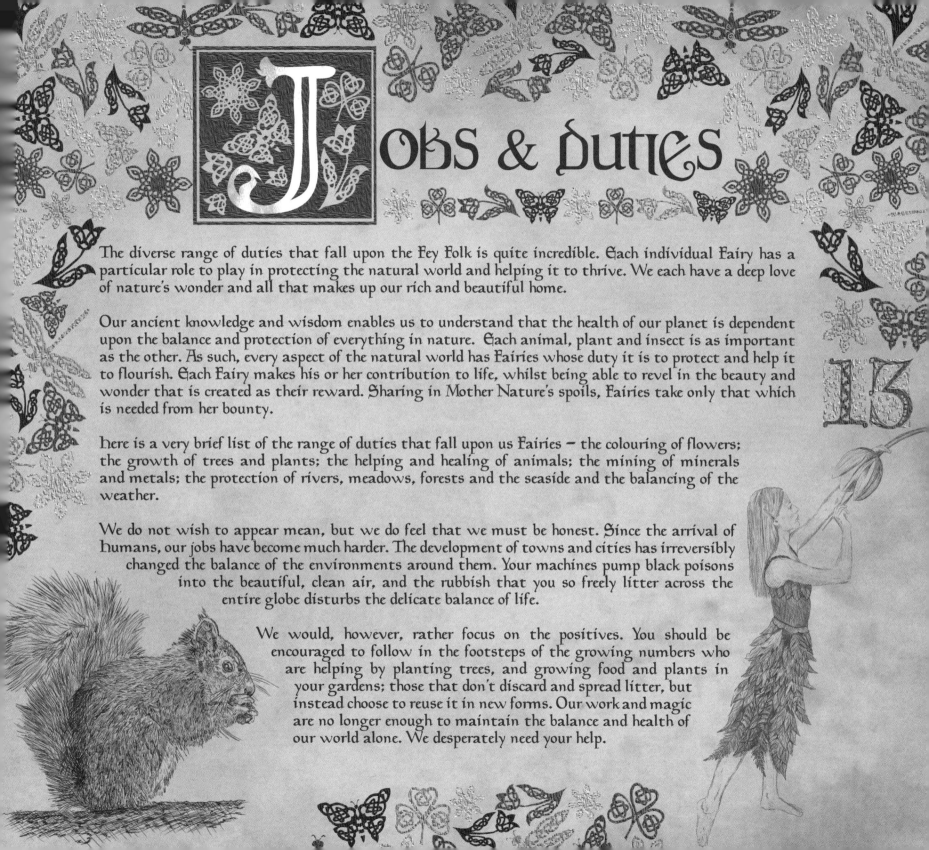

Jobs & Duties

The diverse range of duties that fall upon the Fey Folk is quite incredible. Each individual Fairy has a particular role to play in protecting the natural world and helping it to thrive. We each have a deep love of nature's wonder and all that makes up our rich and beautiful home.

Our ancient knowledge and wisdom enables us to understand that the health of our planet is dependent upon the balance and protection of everything in nature. Each animal, plant and insect is as important as the other. As such, every aspect of the natural world has Fairies whose duty it is to protect and help it to flourish. Each Fairy makes his or her contribution to life, whilst being able to revel in the beauty and wonder that is created as their reward. Sharing in Mother Nature's spoils, Fairies take only that which is needed from her bounty.

Here is a very brief list of the range of duties that fall upon us Fairies – the colouring of flowers; the growth of trees and plants; the helping and healing of animals; the mining of minerals and metals; the protection of rivers, meadows, forests and the seaside and the balancing of the weather.

We do not wish to appear mean, but we do feel that we must be honest. Since the arrival of humans, our jobs have become much harder. The development of towns and cities has irreversibly changed the balance of the environments around them. Your machines pump black poisons into the beautiful, clean air, and the rubbish that you so freely litter across the entire globe disturbs the delicate balance of life.

We would, however, rather focus on the positives. You should be encouraged to follow in the footsteps of the growing numbers who are helping by planting trees, and growing food and plants in your gardens; those that don't discard and spread litter, but instead choose to reuse it in new forms. Our work and magic are no longer enough to maintain the balance and health of our world alone. We desperately need your help.

13

Fairy Magic

We know that Fairy magic, or glamour, has always intrigued humans. Fairies are indeed blessed with the ability to influence things in the natural world, using our ancient knowledge and abilities, or as you call it "magic". An example of this is how we are able to change the appearance of not only ourselves but the things around us too.

Your distant ancestors believed in and had an understanding of what you now call magic. Its use was as commonplace as the wind and the rain – just another natural force. As time progressed and humans became more advanced, the age-old beliefs and rituals of magic began to fall by the wayside, gradually being replaced by what you now refer to as science.

If you find the concept of Fairy magic hard to understand, just think about how the world you live in now would have appeared to humans centuries ago. What would they have thought of modern inventions, such as aeroplanes, mobile phones, televisions and the Internet, all of which you take for granted? We imagine that your scientific developments would have seemed like powerful magic to them.

If you consider it carefully, magic is not too dissimilar to science. It is simply based on the fact that Fairies have existed far longer than humans and thus have a more ancient understanding of the laws of the universe and how they effect the world around us. These are just areas that your scientists have chosen not to fully explore as yet. However, that time is coming and it will prove to be a time of great enlightenment and discovery for the entire human race.

So, you now know that Fairy magic is simply the manipulation of the natural energy and forces that exist all around us. It is something that, with learning and time, you and all humanity will also be able to master.

Communication

Most Fairies would like to help you, but in order to do so we need to be able to communicate. It is for this reason that humans have always and will always be able to talk to Fairies.

Fairies bring you messages of help and guidance, often from within yourselves. We try to help you understand your lives. By enabling you to work out the answers for yourself, we believe that you will gain a greater understanding of the world around you. As such, we will rarely give you a straightforward answer or message. Instead, we use our love of music, wordplay, riddles, dreams, metaphors and visions to communicate with you.

The physical form that we adopt can offer an indication as to our message, with what we wear or possess also holding a clue. It is for you to work out the answer or message, but remember that in order for us to assist you, you must first ask us.

There are many ways in which you can invite interaction with Fairies. The simplest way is to spend time in nature. Relaxing or meditating against a tree or growing plants in your home are two such ways. Always respect nature and do your best to assist in its preservation. Take part in creative activities, such as painting, drawing, music or craft projects. Essentially, enjoyment of any creative endeavour will encourage the Fairies to draw closer. Alternatively, you could leave an area of your garden to grow wild, so that the Fairies can play freely there.

Being generous and kind to others will always bring Fairy favour. Listening to music and singing are also pastimes that the Fairies enjoy. The most important thing to remember when wishing to communicate with the Fey Folk is to invite it, be happy and never lose touch with the playful and joyous child within.

Types of Fairy

Fairies align themselves to the four main elements — Water, Air, Fire and Earth. Your ancestors understood the power of these elements. They were aware of how they could use them to summon up individual powers and, most importantly, they knew that for harmony to exist there had to be a balance between the four.

Earth Fairies:

Earth Fairies are probably the most stable of the Fairy types, reflecting the strong nature of the rocks, root systems, caves, quarries, mines, hills and barrows which they occupy. You may know Earth Fairies better by the names — Dwarves, Gnomes, Knockers, Brownies, Goblins, Pixies and Elves. Their skill as craftsman and their ability to work with natural materials, such as stone, metal and wood, is legendary.

Water Fairies:

Water Fairies are more changeable beings, reflecting the constant ebb and flow of the tides where they reside and the continual movement of the water. They can be found in most places where pure water, whether it be salty or fresh, is located — lakes, the sea shore, the ocean, rivers, canals, pools, springs, wells and fountains. Sites with running water, such as where springs bubble up from the Earth or where waterfalls tumble into the rivers below, are especially powerful.

You may know Water Fairies better by some of the names you have created for them — Nymphs, Sirens, Mermaids, Mermen, Selkies and Sprites. Water is magical in itself, being the giver of all life and holding powerful healing properties, especially if blessed by a Fairy. But in contrast, water has the ability to be horrendously destructive through storms, powerful waves and floods. Water Fairies often reflect the dual nature of water; some may be benevolent towards sailors and fisherman, while others display more destructive tendencies, choosing to dash a ship against the rocks.

Fire Fairies:

Fire Fairies are often very powerful, but again their power has two sides to its nature. They can be found in places of extreme heat, such as deserts, savannahs and volcanoes, inside lightning or riding the sun's rays. They can be found anywhere where there is fire, from bonfires or fireworks through to the flickering flame of a solitary candle.

Some of the names you may know Fire Fairies better by include Salamanders, Djinn and Fire Drakes. Man has long venerated fire; its mystical properties captivating you from the very first time the Fire Fairies chose to introduce you to one of nature's most powerful gifts.

Fire Fairies can reflect the life giving power of the sun, the feeling of warmth and light from a log fire in the dark of night, the power to purify and drive out illness and the ability to turn anything to ash or melt that which will not burn.

Air Fairies:

Air Fairies are perhaps a more advanced Fairy form, combining aspects of all four elements. They have the ability to transcend all levels. Air Fairies can move the earth and topple trees; they can give rise to immense waves, even penetrate water itself in the form of bubbles; they can spread and inject life into fire and at the same time extinguish it.

Perhaps it is this cross-elemental quality and advanced form that gives rise to your preoccupation with the winged Fairy. Air Fairies are sometimes the messengers of the soul, representing the spirit freed from the shackles of an earthly bond with the ability to fly between worlds.

Air Fairies can influence almost everything on our planet. They can bring you a gentle cool breeze on a hot summers day, carry seeds to new pastures and bring the clouds to deliver life-giving rains. They can also however bring hurricanes, tornadoes and sandstorms, devastating all that lies in their path.

Children

It is children who hold the key to the future within their hands. To bring joy to a child is considered to be the most magical of things to a Fairy. This is because, as the Elves at the North Pole say, "When a child smiles, the whole world smiles with them".

Children offer the greatest hope to the world. We Fairies are aware that the actions of tomorrow will be determined by the children of today. This is one of the reasons that we have such a great love for children. Their souls are untainted by the cynical and somewhat limited mind-sets that adult humans seem to adopt as they grow older. The nature of children is much more Fairy like, being playful and carefree. Their minds are fresh and new, uncluttered by the logic and learning that narrows the minds of many older humans. They are more open to the other realms around them and are often able to see and interact with Fairies.

Fairies love happiness and laughter, and children spend more time playing freely in nature. Instead of wanting to complete a particular task, such as mowing the lawn, they simply want to have fun, go on adventures, get dirty, climb trees and let their imaginations carry them away on an infinite wave of possibility.

Fairy experiences are not exclusive to children by any means. Adults, if open minded and kind of heart, are just as welcome to see and work with Fairies. We must mention, however, that the more adults allow children to be exposed to powerful man made stimuli, such as televisions and computers, the harder it becomes for children's minds to experience the full range of natural phenomena.

Parents can help by being open to the experiences recounted by their children. Children automatically look to their parents and teachers as role models, due to the fact that they are their primary source of information about the world. As such, it could prove extremely beneficial if adults were to encourage children to search for, assist and interact with Fairies.

18

Fairy Godmother

From the first time we began to realise that humans were going to have a major influence on the fate of the world, the Fairy Realm decided to try to help and protect you. It was thus determined that a human Guardian, or Fairy Godmother, as you refer to them, would be assigned to each new-born child.

The Fairies selected to do this would need to have achieved a status of worthiness and shown themselves capable of helping to guide the fate of our planet through human hands. It is considered a high position within the Fairy Realm to become a human Guardian.

The role of a Fairy Godmother in determining a child's fate has been subject to much speculation over the centuries. Fairies do not think it right to interfere in human lives to too great an extent. Rather, Fairy Godmothers bestow a special gift upon each child when they are born. This gift is a special skill or talent that, if unlocked, will lead to a magical life of great achievement and wonder. The Fairies can only plant the seed; it is your job to help it to grow by leading a good and wholesome life.

Along with the giving of your special gift, the duties of your Fairy Godmother also include protection, particularly against the influence of Dark Fairies. They can also bestow good fortune, offer guidance and at times, even grant wishes.

Fairies consider childhood to be the most important phase of life. Because of this, it is also the time when your Fairy Godmother will be most present. As you grow older and become wiser, you are more able to make your own way in the world.

Fairy Godmothers stay assigned to you throughout your lives and if you remain open to them and their magical help and advice, they will continue to guide and protect you.

Fairy Year

Imbolc: February 2nd – Northern Hemisphere / July 31st – Southern Hemisphere

With the sparkling of frost, the lengthening of the days and the first signs of life beginning to emerge from hibernation, Imbolc signifies the crossover point from the dark depths of winter to the start of a new cycle of life. It is a festival of cleansing and making way for the new. Lighting candles and sharing in the Fairies' celebrations will invite blessings into your home – especially if you have tidied and cleared it of clutter.

Spring Equinox: 21st March – Northern Hemisphere / 21st September – Southern Hemisphere

This is a very busy festival for the Fairies, as they are engaged in looking after the new, emerging lives of both plants and animals. It is a good time to tidy your garden, removing the dead to allow the emergence of the new. Also, planting seeds, or even a tree, will bring favour from the Fairies at Spring Equinox. Singing and talking to your new plants can help by drawing the Fairies in to assist you.

Beltane: 30th April – Northern Hemisphere / 31st October – Southern Hemisphere

Beltane is one of the most joyful and expressive of Fairy festivals, as it occurs when nature is blossoming and bursting forth with life. At this time of year, Fairies love to dance among the bluebell glades or frolic in the sunshine, as they revel in the beauty of nature. The Fairies' hard work in spring is beginning to reap its rewards and most of us Fey Folk are very active at this time.

Midsummer: 22nd June – Northern Hemisphere / December 22nd – Southern Hemisphere

One of the most magical times of the year, when the sun is at the height of its power and the days are at their longest. Flowers and plants are in full bloom and the Fairies use this festival to celebrate the peak of life and all the world's energy. It is an important crossover point, as the world begins to move towards winter and the darker days once more.

Lammas: 31st July – Northern hemisphere / 2nd February – Southern hemisphere
This is a particularly busy time of year for the Fairies, as preparations for harvest and the coming winter begin. Fairies often move their home to their place of winter residence at this time and processions of Fairies may be seen travelling along ancient Fairy roads. Bake a loaf of bread and ask for the blessing of a Fairy to help your bread to rise and with it your life's fortunes. Be sure to leave out some of the freshly baked goods for them to enjoy.

Autumn Equinox: 21st September – Northern hemisphere / 2nd March – Southern hemisphere
At this time, the natural world stands on the brink of light and dark, with the darkness gaining stronger momentum. It is a time of hard work for the Fairies once again, as the berry studded hedgerows reflect the abundance of nature. It is the time of harvest and preparation for the winter. Make sure that you leave an offering of fruit and vegetables for the Fairies at this time of the year, as this is sure to bring their favour upon you.

Samhain: 31st October – Northern hemisphere / 30th April – Southern hemisphere
This is the point when the veil between all worlds is at its thinnest, enabling the free flow of Fairies and all types of spirits between realms. Known to many of you in the Northern hemisphere as halloween, it marks the official start of winter and marks the end of another cycle of life. Many Fairies retire from sight after this festival, returning to their own realm. As such, Fairy mounds and doorways may be found open.

Yule: 22nd December – Northern hemisphere / 22nd June – Southern hemisphere
The Midwinter Solstice sees a new cycle of life begin as the days lengthen again, signalling the return of light. Fairies love Yule, or the season of Christmas, as many of you humans now call it. It is a time of happiness and celebration, with much giving, love and laughter. Decorating your home and tree is a magical ritual that is looked upon favourably by the Fairies – especially when you use Fairy lights or place a Fairy at the top of your tree.

Dark Fairies

For all things to exist there must be a balance between the positive and the negative; there can be no light without dark and no good without bad. The same is true of Fairies.

Firstly, it is our duty to warn you that Dark Fairies are real and that even good Fairies sometimes do bad things. It is in our nature, as it is yours. If you are honest with yourself, you will have to admit that even you are not good all of the time.

The good news is that most Fairies are more mischievous than they are mean. They enjoy playing pranks, such as hiding things or making you stub your toe. The Dark Fairies, however, can bring illness upon your house and cause major disruption in your lives, if you let them.

Many Dark Fairies live deep underground or in isolated lonely places, such as forests or caves. Known to humans by names such as Gremlins, Trolls, Goblins or Orcs, these are often Fairies that have been cast out from their Troops or communities because of their dark nature. Their dark existence and thoughts can eventually bring about a shadowy and twisted appearance in their physical form.

These often-spiteful creatures are as much a danger to Fairies as they are to humans. Many Dark Fairies have taken issue with human existence, particularly in protest against your technological and mechanical advances. They feel, you see, that you are the biggest cause of the changes in the world that they detest the most. So, when a car or machine has problems, there will likely be a Dark Fairy at the root of it. They often look to create havoc in the human world.

The best way to protect yourself from the influence of Dark Fairies is simply to maximise your laughter and happiness. Also, try to avoid places where you feel the presence of a Dark Fairy. If an area feels as though it has a bad energy, if grass and plants do not grow there or there is no bird or animal life, then be wary as it may be home to a Dark Fairy.

Food & Drink

Fairies can exist in two main forms. We are, in our most natural form, ethereal beings made of pure energy, but, in order to have an impact upon the physical aspects of the world, we must at times adopt physical bodies.

For you, food is energy; for the plants and animals that you know, food is energy. You eat food and your body converts it into the energy you require to go about your daily lives — to grow, to move and to think. Everything you do requires this energy.

Fairies only need to eat in order to adopt a physical form; we don't need to eat food in our natural pure energy state. When we do eat, we only consume vegetable based foods. We eat that which is given freely by nature and drink only fresh water, — whether it comes directly from a bubbling spring or the morning dew that has gathered upon a waxy leaf.

We enjoy a variety of foods, but one of our favourite treats is to sip the nectar from flowers. We are also particularly fond of honey and barley. Given the fact that we generally adopt much smaller bodies than humans and spend far less time in physical form, we do not require much food to sustain us.

Something that Fairies have long known and that we feel we must share with you is that water takes on the form of the energy that it is exposed to. Given that most natural food sources have a very high water content, this means that the same is true of your food. Happiness and positivity will cause the water particles to take on a healthy and beneficial form, whereas disruption and negativity can cause the water, and thus the food containing it, to have harmful effects on your body.

By saying thank you to nature and showing gratitude for the food you are lucky enough to be eating, you will ensure that its magical properties have a positive effect on your bodies.

25

Fairy Stories

The wide range of folklore and Fairy Tales that have endured the test of time provide a deep insight into the character and personalities of Fairies. These stories were originally used to provide clues to those who proved themselves worthy by revealing the secrets of how to approach and work with us.

Listening or reading about Fairies in stories, songs or poetry is a means of telling us that you are interested and open to us. This is a good first step to making contact. However, one secret that few humans have discovered, even after all these centuries, is that you can use these tales as a form of meditation through which to communicate with us. We only reveal this to you now because, as mentioned before, it is our aim to try to re-establish the bond between our two realms.

This concept may seem a little far-fetched from your normal way of thinking, but let us assure you that this is a powerful method that can unlock the hidden doors to our realm.

To begin, focus on your favourite Fairy Tale, one that you have read several times before. It is always best to perform any such attempt at communicating with Fairies in a place of nature; a place where you can put your hands and feet on the earth.

Close your eyes and relax; feel yourself forming a connection to the earth. Place your hands on the earth and really feel it. Imagine a slow deep pulse rising, as though you can feel the beating heart of the planet. As this happens, know that you are safe and protected.

With your eyes still closed, picture in your mind that you are standing within a circle of ancient oak trees. Their sheer size and scale makes you feel tiny. Their bark is twisted and gnarled, like the skin of some giant life entity. The tops of the roots are exposed, but you know that these roots penetrate deep into the earth itself. As you stare up at these majestic beings, you are filled with wonder and delight. Believe that if ever trees would be home to Fairies, it would be these trees.

As you turn around at the centre of this circle of magical trees, notice a soft mist rising from the ground. Keep smiling as the mist forms and slowly covers the grass, before coating the bases of the mighty oak trees. As the magical mist closes in around you, smell its beautiful flower fragrance, as it brings a sweet flavour of honey to your lips and swirls around your head. The mist will completely envelop the ancient oaks, before it begins to fade away again.

You will no longer be in that magical glen, but will see yourself as the main character of your chosen Fairy Tale. See yourself stepping into the storyline and experiencing each part of the story. Interact with all the characters, animals, Fairies and magical beings within the tale.

It is not essential that you follow the storyline completely; allow your imagination to adjust the story in any way you wish.

As the story ends, visualise the mist rising up and surrounding you again. When the mist recedes once more, you will find yourself back in the centre of the circle of oak trees. Know that this is a shadow land; a bridge between the worlds of human and Fairy.

Draw a slow, deep, breath, letting the scene fade before you. Feel yourself back on that same spot where you first began your journey. Keeping your eyes closed, feel the earth once more beneath your hands.

Slowly open your eyes and with a soft focus look gently around you. Are there any moving shadows or faces in the bushes? Glowing spots? Don't worry that you may be seeing things; there is no imagination without its roots in reality.

Thank the earth and the nature around you for the experience and for the magic that is yet to come.

Plants & Animals

Plants enrich all areas of the planet, carpeting it in a blanket of life. Reaching from the highest mountain, where no person or animal can survive, through to the forests, deserts, gardens and deepest depths of the oceans. Plants capture the sun's magnificent power and transform it into the food and energy that sustains not only other plants, but all animal and human life as well. Plants provide you with food, clothes, drinks and medicines, as well as many other things that you could not live without, including the very air that you breath.

By far the largest and most influential of all the plants are trees. Trees are the lungs of the planet; they produce the wood you use to build your homes, burn on your fires and make your furniture from. They are also the source of the oil and coal that have long powered your machines.

Trees are sacred to Fairies; they even have their own spirits known as Dryads. Where the Fairy triad of oak, ash and hawthorn grow, there is sure to be a strong Fairy presence. Many trees form a portal to other realms and offer homes to us Fey Folk. Your ancestors once knew of their ancient wisdom, and, even now, with this bond dwindling, children have a great affinity for trees. They love to shelter and play beneath them, to climb and scamper throughout their branches. Trees can help to increase your intuition, while bringing wisdom, knowledge and deep peace. Also, unbeknownst to your scientists, they release chemicals into the air that are freely available to anyone and can help heal all sorts of ills. Yet, despite all of this, you still do not hold them in the regard they deserve.

Fairies have an eternal bond with plants and many of us focus our lives around helping them. We carry out many duties, in order to help them to thrive. We help enrich the soil for them; create colours and scent;

look after gardens, fields and woodland, and nurture dormant plants until it is time for them to grow and blossom once more.

Plants are an important way of bridging the divide between the Fairy and Human Realms. By growing and caring for plants, you are sure to draw the presence and favour of Fairies.

Along with plants, animals can also be found in every nook and cranny of the world. There are mammals and birds, fish and insects; each and every one of them integral to the Wheel of Life. Fairies have a great affinity with the animal world and often shift their physical form to that of an animal. In this way, we are able to influence the physical realm without drawing too much undue attention to ourselves and keep our true form and purpose a secret. Some of the favoured animal forms adopted by Fairies include – deer, dragonflies, butterflies, seals and birds.

Whilst animals live alongside humans, often sharing very close relationships, they are fundamentally, very different to you. They live their lives in a simple and honest manner, free from the bindings of your material world. For the most part, they live in complete harmony with nature, doing and taking only that which is needed to survive and enjoy their existence. As such, this brings the blessing and support of the Fairy Realm and places them under our protection.

In ancient times, humans believed animals to be teachers and guardians of Mankind. They were revered and adopted by your people as symbols of power and ancient knowledge. Now, it seems that many of you treat them as little more than another resource to be used for your own benefit. Whilst humans are unable to survive without the many wonderful plants and animals of the world, we have watched with heavy hearts at your mistreatment of them. It is important that you learn that what you bring upon others, whether animal, plant or fellow human, will eventually befall yourself.

Healing

Because of our ancient understanding of the natural world, Fairies are well placed to offer powers of healing. It is a role that many Fairies play. We help to heal plants, animals and ecosystems, which of course, means that we can help humans as well.

One thing that you may not realise is that your body is made of stardust. The make up of your physical being and how it works is a reflection of the natural world as a whole. To understand your body is to understand the Universe.

Your body requires balance in order to maintain health. Full health is achieved by having all elements in perfect equilibrium. When this balance is disrupted, it can lead to illness. The particles that make up all parts of your body are, in their simplest form, pure energy. By consequence, you too are a being of pure energy. Harmony in your energy field, which can be seen by some as an aura, is the key to your health. The external influences of your modern world, with machines, technology and chemicals, mean that it is now much more difficult to maintain the required physical balance.

The Fairies charged with the duty of healing are light based creatures; they rarely appear in physical bodies. They would rather not waste their valuable energy by manifesting in this form. They prefer instead to maintain their higher vibrational frequency and channel the infinite energy of the cosmos into the plant, animal or human they are healing, much like the charging of a battery.

There are many ways that you can help to maintain your own good health. Eat good natural foods and include lots of fruit and vegetables. This will ensure that your body has the right ingredients with which to make itself strong. You should be happy as often as possible and grateful for your health, as illness cannot take a grip in a happy, harmonious body.

Fairy music

Music has always been an integral part of Fairy life, right from the very beginning of time. The reason that we love music so much is that it embodies vibration and harmony, which are the essence of all creation. Music is a truly universal language, bringing together all types of being to a place of common experience and understanding, without the need for any words.

Each type of Fairy has a particular fondness for a certain group of instruments and style of music: Earth Fairies favour percussion, drums, rattles, gongs, bells and brass; Water Fairies enjoy chimes, tubular bells, strings and the singing voice; Air Fairies have a preference for wind instruments, flutes and wind chimes and Fire Fairies favour lyres, harps, the sistrum and the composition process. These instruments are favoured because each produces a vibration or sound that matches the resonating frequency of the Fairies' own existence and being.

With the endless millennia that Fairies have had to practice and perfect the playing of music, the Fairy Realm is able to boast many accomplished musicians. Whilst each of the four main types of Fairy have their preference, when all four elements come together to form a Fairy orchestra, it achieves the ultimate perfection. This is reflected in the harmony of the elements in the world beyond.

Fairies have always bestowed gifts of musical ability upon humans, in order to help bring about positive change. Worthy individuals who show an early natural propensity for music have often been blessed with Fairy gifts of musical talent.

If we could offer a piece of advice to all humans, it would be to never lose your love of music. Music truly is magic at work; it has the power to alter your existence. The path of your life is determined by your emotions and your mind-set. Music is one thing that has the ability to alter your mood. It can relax you, inspire you or energise you. As such, music can help to alter the course of your life for the better. All you have to do is embrace it.

Conclusion

Since the very beginning of man's time on Earth, Fairies have watched on with great interest as you have grown and evolved. We lived for many thousands of years in complete harmony together, human and Fairy side by side. However, as most things tend to, gradually this relationship changed. You grew rapidly, using your vast intelligence and abilities to constantly alter and develop the way you live your lives. And, as you changed, so too did the landscape of the entire planet around you. In more recent times, your development has begun to threaten the very place that we call home, and with it, all of Earth's inhabitants.

Whilst many Fairies have shied away from human interaction, there are those of us who are eager to rebuild our once unbreakable bond. We wish to once again work hand in hand with humans; we hope to guide you and also for you to assist us. Your destruction of nature and the way you live your lives must change now before it is too late.

With the writing of this book, we hope to once again open the channels of communication between Fairy and human. Our magic and ancient knowledge of nature and the world around us is freely available to those of you who wish to discover it. If we appear to you and allow you to see us, it will most likely be because we want to give you some kind of message.

There are many Fairies who do not understand or speak your languages. Also, much time has elapsed since communication between us was commonplace and this has led to many more of us losing touch with your great number of words. A lot of Fairies still use the same ancient symbols to communicate, but not all have yet realised that the majority of you have lost the understanding that your ancestors once had. Examples of such symbols can include appearing with wings, wands, crowns or swords. Wings, for instance, are an ancient symbol of transcendence, representing the power to move

between worlds. With this, we might be telling you to rise above the bonds of the material world and view things from above; to take a new perspective on your life. We believe that the best way to for all creatures to learn is for them to work out the lessons for themselves. This means that we will rarely give you a straightforward answer or message. Instead, we use imagery, wordplay and riddles to provoke deeper thought on a given subject.

As we hope you can now see, in order for our worlds to realign once more, both Fairy and human are going to have to work much harder. Only then, will we once again be able to fully understand one another.

Monuments to the effectiveness of our ancient relationship can be found across the globe, from the Pyramids to Stonehenge. Despite our concerns with human behaviour and the damage it is causing, it is your positive attributes and strengths that promise a brighter future. Your intelligence, your great capacity for love and the compassion that we see many of you show to animals, plants and each other, along with your ability to change the course of nature on an immense scale, are the reasons that many of us haven't given up hope. You have the power to change yourselves, each other and the fate of all of us. We would be honoured to offer our help in achieving this; to unite once more and return balance to our beautiful home.

We hope to help you heal yourselves, as when you heal yourself, you heal the world around you. It is our quest to help you rediscover the wondrous magic of our home, but this journey must first begin with you rediscovering the magic within yourselves.